I CAN'T SLEEP

KNOCK KNOCK®

VENICE, CALIFORNIA

Created and published by Knock Knock
Distributed by Who's There, Inc.
Venice, CA 90291
knockknockstuff.com

ISBN: 978-160106106-5
UPC: 825703-50022-6

10 9 8 7

YOU'RE STILL AWAKE

Really, with so much fodder requiring your obsessive consideration every day, who can blame you? Whether you're preoccupied with finances, matters of the heart, life goals, or the innumerable errands that should have been run last week, when the clock strikes midnight—or 3:00 AM—taming those wild thoughts so you can get some shut-eye can be a Herculean task.

Although you may toil through the night by yourself, you're not alone—insomnia affects tens of millions of people. According to the Mayo Clinic, more than a third of adults have sleep-related issues at one point or another, and 10 to 15 percent are chronic insomniacs. The National Sleep Foundation found that only 28 percent of us get the full eight hours that experts recommend. Provided with the right tools, however, we can all harness the peace and quiet that only a night sky and non-business hours can provide—maybe even catching a few winks when all's said and done.

Naturally, insomnia's causes are as many and varied as its sufferers, ranging from common psychological difficulties (stress, depression, or anxiety) to illnesses (hormonal imbalances, aches and pains, or just a stuffy nose), as well as environmental factors (eating a heavy meal, living above a nightclub, or a snoring bed partner). While problems associated with a lack of sleep are well documented, including mental fogginess and weight gain, there are also potential upsides. According to sleep researcher Jerome Siegel, insomnia may be nature's way of improving our time management; we sleep only when we need to and are awake when we're most inclined to be productive.

This claim is corroborated by the number of famous, incredibly prolific insomniacs. For example, despite (or perhaps because of) suffering bouts of sleeplessness throughout his life, Marcel Proust completed a seven-volume novel, *Remembrance of Things Past*, most of which he wrote in bed. William Shakespeare struggled with insomnia and finished almost forty classic plays. Notable world leaders such as Winston Churchill, Benjamin Franklin, and Napoleon Bonaparte most likely conducted the majority of their affairs in a sleep-deprived state.

But what should you do when the sleep just won't come? Home remedies have been vanquishing sleepless nights for eons, including sipping warm milk, taking a bath before bed, and listening to soothing music. The effectiveness of these tactics, however, is hardly proven, and learning to channel your sleeplessness productively like the luminaries above may be your best strategy. Whether you're trying to embrace the midnight hours or sleep through them, no plan of attack is more manageable and universally available than the journal. As sleep technologist Lauren Butler says, "People with insomnia lie in bed and think, think, think. If they put a notepad by the bed, they can write down all the stuff they're thinking about—the grocery list, pay that bill—so they can release it."

In addition to providing an outlet for focusing your spiraling thoughts in the middle of the night, journal writing has been shown to have other powerful benefits. According to a widely cited study by James W. Pennebaker and Janel D. Seagal, "Writing about important personal experiences in an emotional way… brings about improvements in mental and physical health." Proven physical benefits include stress management, strengthened immune systems, fewer doctor visits, and improvement in chronic illnesses such as asthma (clearly it's better to vent than to hyperventilate)—all of which can lead to a better night's sleep.

It's not entirely clear how journaling accomplishes all this. Experts agree that catharsis is involved, but they also point to the importance of organizing experiences into a narrative. According to *Newsweek*, some experts believe that journaling "forces us to transform the ruminations cluttering our minds into coherent stories. Writing about an experience may also dull its emotional impact," which can help you shut off those thoughts long enough to catch some Zs. In many ways, journaling can be seen as a way of organizing the conscious stuff floating around your brain before the committee of sleep can do its part with the subconscious.

As a devotee of this journal, you're obviously having some problems sleeping, and you have a lot on your mind. That could just mean that you're smarter than the blithely snoozing masses and have more to say than they do (studies have found that night owls are, in fact, more intelligent and have better memories than early risers). You've got time to fill, thoughts to process, and you've chosen to use the fertile night hours to their greatest potential. To take advantage of the journaling process fully, however, don't simply vent that you can't get to sleep, as that may exacerbate your frustration with the elusive sandman. Instead, get your feelings out and then try to understand them. Here are a few additional tips to consider. Experts agree that in order to reap the benefits of journaling, you have to stick with it, quasi-daily, for as little as five minutes at a time, even if you're not struggling to fall asleep. Set up a routine of writing before bedtime (perhaps with a nightcap of milk and cognac, à la Theodore Roosevelt). Prompt your writing with questions. Elaborate on "Why I can't sleep" and "Insights only possible at the end of the day." The *I Can't Sleep* journal's quotations will also provide a jumping-off point for your writing. Don't criticize your writing as you journal; journaling is a process of self-reflection, not a structured composition. In other words, spew. Finally, determine a home for your journal where others won't find it—such as under the pillow you'll eventually rest your head on.

Famed novelist Saul Bellow once declared, "You never have to change anything you got up in the middle of the night to write," and he won a Nobel Prize. Follow that observation, and not only will you usher forth written brilliance, but you'll also be well on your way to conquering your sleepless nights.

Life is something that happens when you can't get to sleep.

FRAN LEBOWITZ

WHY I CAN'T SLEEP TONIGHT:

It has been a good semester. ~~Both~~ Masonry & Dynamics were fun for me. In masonry we got all the way through shear walls. The final dynamics homework was to solve the forced MDOF problem. That seemed very good for the students (& me). I can't wait to ~~experience~~ have this semester again. Just a full year. & it will be Spring 2015. who knows, maybe we will have an adopted/~~a~~natural birth child.

I'm not sleeping because I'm excited to have family time & have finals done. Tim & I had an owly chat. when he wanted to put up the Christmas tree and our family room was a disaster & dinner (was not started, I went a bit crazy. We agreed to set up the TV before decorating for Christmas. Hopefully that will be this evening. Tim loves Christmas & put the tree in water downstairs so it does not freeze.

I realize that from the cradle up I have been like the rest of the race—never quite sane in the night.

MARK TWAIN

WHY I CAN'T SLEEP TONIGHT:

12/9/13

Who says you were sane during the day, Mr Twain? In general, our society worships productivity and being busy all of the time. Could this be why I struggle to relax? Cardio exercises are touted for ♡ benefits, but what about yoga, or Pilates? Strengthening our core is so important. Over break, I'm going to swim at the RIC.

I feel terrible about loosing my patience with Bridget. On the other hand, my needs are not being met. We have been without a calibration of the ELE for some time now, over 6 months. She asked if I wanted the plot in force or volts. When I drew the calib. graph last week, she insisted that she would remember. Today she asked for direction. What is up? Help me to understand her health issues are clouding her work performance.

The last refuge of the insomniac is a sense of superiority to the sleeping world.

LEONARD COHEN

WHY I CAN'T SLEEP TONIGHT:

_____
_____
_____
_____
_____
_____
_____
_____
_____
_____
_____
_____
_____
_____
_____
_____
_____
_____
_____
_____
_____
_____
_____
_____
_____

WHEN TOMORROW OFFICIALLY BECOMES TODAY:

I'm for anything that gets you through the night, be it prayer, tranquilizers, or a bottle of Jack Daniel's.

FRANK SINATRA

WHY I CAN'T SLEEP TONIGHT:

_____

_____

_____

_____

_____

_____

_____

_____

_____

_____

_____

_____

_____

_____

_____

_____

_____

_____

_____

_____

_____

_____

_____

_____

_____

_____

_____

WHEN TOMORROW OFFICIALLY BECOMES TODAY:

To begin with, the average, healthy, well-adjusted adult gets up at seven-thirty in the morning feeling just plain terrible.

JEAN KERR

DATE

WHY I CAN'T SLEEP TONIGHT:

_____
_____
_____
_____
_____
_____
_____
_____
_____
_____
_____
_____
_____
_____
_____
_____
_____
_____
_____
_____
_____
_____
_____

WHEN TOMORROW OFFICIALLY BECOMES TODAY:

How do people go to sleep? I'm afraid I've lost the knack.

DOROTHY PARKER

WHY I CAN'T SLEEP TONIGHT:

_____

_____

_____

_____

_____

_____

_____

_____

_____

_____

_____

_____

_____

_____

_____

_____

_____

_____

_____

_____

_____

_____

_____

_____

WHEN TOMORROW OFFICIALLY BECOMES TODAY:

A flock of sheep that leisurely
 pass by,

One after one; the sound of
 rain, and bees

Murmuring; the fall of rivers,
 winds and seas,

Smooth fields, white sheets of
 water, and pure sky;

I have thought of all by turns,
 and yet do lie

Sleepless!

WILLIAM WORDSWORTH

WHY I CAN'T SLEEP TONIGHT:

_____
_____
_____
_____
_____
_____
_____
_____
_____
_____
_____
_____
_____
_____
_____
_____
_____
_____
_____
_____
_____
_____
_____
_____
_____
_____
_____

WHEN TOMORROW OFFICIALLY BECOMES TODAY:

Tonight's forecast: Dark.
Continued dark tonight
turning to partly light
in the morning.

GEORGE CARLIN

DATE

WHY I CAN'T SLEEP TONIGHT:

_____
_____
_____
_____
_____
_____
_____
_____
_____
_____
_____
_____
_____
_____
_____
_____
_____
_____
_____
_____
_____
_____
_____
_____
_____
_____
_____
_____
_____
_____
_____
_____

WHEN TOMORROW OFFICIALLY BECOMES TODAY:

Sleep, that deplorable curtailment of the joy of life.

VIRGINIA WOOLF

DATE

WHY I CAN'T SLEEP TONIGHT:

_____
_____
_____
_____
_____
_____
_____
_____
_____
_____
_____
_____
_____
_____
_____
_____
_____
_____
_____
_____
_____
_____
_____
_____

WHEN TOMORROW OFFICIALLY BECOMES TODAY:

Was it only by dreaming or writing
that I could find out what I thought?

JOAN DIDION

WHY I CAN'T SLEEP TONIGHT:

_____

_____

_____

_____

_____

_____

_____

_____

_____

_____

_____

_____

_____

_____

_____

_____

_____

_____

_____

_____

_____

_____

_____

_____

_____

_____

WHEN TOMORROW OFFICIALLY BECOMES TODAY:

In a real dark night
of the soul it is always
three o'clock in the
morning.

	DATE	

WHY I CAN'T SLEEP TONIGHT:

_____

_____

_____

_____

_____

_____

_____

_____

_____

_____

_____

_____

_____

_____

_____

_____

_____

_____

_____

_____

_____

_____

_____

_____

_____

_____

_____

WHEN TOMORROW OFFICIALLY BECOMES TODAY:

The mind is its own place, and in itself
Can make a Heaven of Hell, a Hell of Heaven.

JOHN MILTON

DATE		

WHY I CAN'T SLEEP TONIGHT:

_____
_____
_____
_____
_____
_____
_____
_____
_____
_____
_____
_____
_____
_____
_____
_____
_____
_____
_____
_____
_____
_____
_____
_____

WHEN TOMORROW OFFICIALLY BECOMES TODAY:

There are times when silence is golden—other times when it is just plain yellow.

ED COLE

	DATE	

WHY I CAN'T SLEEP TONIGHT:

_____
_____
_____
_____
_____
_____
_____
_____
_____
_____
_____
_____
_____
_____
_____
_____
_____
_____
_____
_____
_____
_____
_____
_____
_____

WHEN TOMORROW OFFICIALLY BECOMES TODAY:

It ain't as bad as you think. It will look better in the morning.

COLIN POWELL

DATE

WHY I CAN'T SLEEP TONIGHT:

_____

_____

_____

_____

_____

_____

_____

_____

_____

_____

_____

_____

_____

_____

_____

_____

_____

_____

_____

_____

_____

_____

_____

_____

_____

_____

_____

_____

_____

WHEN TOMORROW OFFICIALLY BECOMES TODAY:

In its early stages, insomnia is almost an oasis in which those who have to think or suffer darkly take refuge.

———

COLETTE

WHY I CAN'T SLEEP TONIGHT:

_____

_____

_____

_____

_____

_____

_____

_____

_____

_____

_____

_____

_____

_____

_____

_____

_____

_____

_____

_____

_____

_____

_____

_____

_____

_____

_____

_____

_____

_____

WHEN TOMORROW OFFICIALLY BECOMES TODAY:

It seemed to be a necessary ritual that he should prepare himself for sleep by meditating under the solemnity of the night sky...a mysterious transaction between the infinity of the soul and the infinity of the universe.

VICTOR HUGO

WHY I CAN'T SLEEP TONIGHT:

_____
_____
_____
_____
_____
_____
_____
_____
_____
_____
_____
_____
_____
_____
_____
_____
_____
_____
_____
_____
_____
_____
_____
_____
_____
_____
_____
_____
_____
_____

WHEN TOMORROW OFFICIALLY BECOMES TODAY:

Most people do not consider dawn to be an attractive experience—unless they are still up.

ELLEN GOODMAN

DATE		

WHY I CAN'T SLEEP TONIGHT:

_____

_____

_____

_____

_____

_____

_____

_____

_____

_____

_____

_____

_____

_____

_____

_____

_____

_____

_____

_____

_____

_____

_____

_____

_____

_____

_____

_____

WHEN TOMORROW OFFICIALLY BECOMES TODAY:

Sometimes I lie awake at night, and I ask, "Where have I gone wrong?" Then a voice says to me, "This is going to take more than one night."

CHARLES M. SCHULZ

WHY I CAN'T SLEEP TONIGHT:

_____

_____

_____

_____

_____

_____

_____

_____

_____

_____

_____

_____

_____

_____

_____

_____

_____

_____

_____

_____

_____

_____

_____

_____

_____

_____

_____

_____

_____

WHEN TOMORROW OFFICIALLY BECOMES TODAY:

Character is what you are in the dark.

DWIGHT L. MOODY

DATE

WHY I CAN'T SLEEP TONIGHT:

_____

_____

_____

_____

_____

_____

_____

_____

_____

_____

_____

_____

_____

_____

_____

_____

_____

_____

_____

_____

_____

_____

_____

_____

_____

_____

WHEN TOMORROW OFFICIALLY BECOMES TODAY:

A little insomnia is not without its value in making us appreciate sleep, in throwing a ray of light upon that darkness.

MARCEL PROUST

WHY I CAN'T SLEEP TONIGHT:

_____

_____

_____

_____

_____

_____

_____

_____

_____

_____

_____

_____

_____

_____

_____

_____

_____

_____

_____

_____

_____

_____

_____

WHEN TOMORROW OFFICIALLY BECOMES TODAY:

No human being believes that any other human being has a right to be in bed when he himself is up.

ROBERT LYND

DATE		

WHY I CAN'T SLEEP TONIGHT:

_____

_____

_____

_____

_____

_____

_____

_____

_____

_____

_____

_____

_____

_____

_____

_____

_____

_____

_____

_____

_____

_____

_____

_____

_____

WHEN TOMORROW OFFICIALLY BECOMES TODAY:

Life is one long process of getting tired.

SAMUEL BUTLER

DATE		

WHY I CAN'T SLEEP TONIGHT:

_____

_____

_____

_____

_____

_____

_____

_____

_____

_____

_____

_____

_____

_____

_____

_____

_____

_____

_____

_____

_____

_____

_____

_____

_____

_____

_____

WHEN TOMORROW OFFICIALLY BECOMES TODAY:

Not being able to sleep is terrible. You have the misery of having partied all night ... without the satisfaction.

LYNN JOHNSTON

DATE		

WHY I CAN'T SLEEP TONIGHT:

_____

_____

_____

_____

_____

_____

_____

_____

_____

_____

_____

_____

_____

_____

_____

_____

_____

_____

_____

_____

_____

_____

_____

_____

_____

_____

WHEN TOMORROW OFFICIALLY BECOMES TODAY:

You know those days when you've got the mean reds...the blues are because you're getting fat or maybe it's been raining too long. You're sad, that's all. But the mean reds are horrible. You're afraid and you sweat like hell, but you don't know what you're afraid of. Except something bad is going to happen, only you don't know what it is.

TRUMAN CAPOTE

WHY I CAN'T SLEEP TONIGHT:

A good gulp of hot whiskey at bedtime— it's not very scientific, but it helps.

SIR ALEXANDER FLEMING

DATE

WHY I CAN'T SLEEP TONIGHT:

_____

_____

_____

_____

_____

_____

_____

_____

_____

_____

_____

_____

_____

_____

_____

_____

_____

_____

_____

_____

_____

_____

_____

_____

_____

_____

_____

_____

WHEN TOMORROW OFFICIALLY BECOMES TODAY:

I hate it when my foot falls asleep during the day, because that means it's going to be up all night.

STEVEN WRIGHT

WHY I CAN'T SLEEP TONIGHT:

WHEN TOMORROW OFFICIALLY BECOMES TODAY:

Bed is the best place for reading, thinking, or doing nothing.

DORIS LESSING

DATE		

WHY I CAN'T SLEEP TONIGHT:

_____

_____

_____

_____

_____

_____

_____

_____

_____

_____

_____

_____

_____

_____

_____

_____

_____

_____

_____

_____

_____

_____

_____

_____

_____

_____

_____

_____

_____

_____

WHEN TOMORROW OFFICIALLY BECOMES TODAY:

If you see ten troubles coming down the road, you can be sure that nine will run into the ditch before they reach you.

CALVIN COOLIDGE

DATE

WHY I CAN'T SLEEP TONIGHT:

_____

_____

_____

_____

_____

_____

_____

_____

_____

_____

_____

_____

_____

_____

_____

_____

_____

_____

_____

_____

_____

_____

_____

WHEN TOMORROW OFFICIALLY BECOMES TODAY:

It is better to light one candle than to curse the darkness.

JAMES KELLER

DATE		

WHY I CAN'T SLEEP TONIGHT:

_____

_____

_____

_____

_____

_____

_____

_____

_____

_____

_____

_____

_____

_____

_____

_____

_____

_____

_____

_____

_____

_____

_____

_____

WHEN TOMORROW OFFICIALLY BECOMES TODAY:

Nighttime is really the best time to work. All the ideas are there to be yours because everyone else is asleep.

CATHERINE O'HARA

WHY I CAN'T SLEEP TONIGHT:

WHEN TOMORROW OFFICIALLY BECOMES TODAY:

Sleeping is no mean art: for its sake one must stay awake all day.

FRIEDRICH NIETZSCHE

WHY I CAN'T SLEEP TONIGHT:

_____
_____
_____
_____
_____
_____
_____
_____
_____
_____
_____
_____
_____
_____
_____
_____
_____
_____
_____
_____
_____
_____
_____
_____
_____

WHEN TOMORROW OFFICIALLY BECOMES TODAY:

When I really worry about something, I don't just fool around. I even have to go to the bathroom when I worry about something. Only, I don't go. I'm too worried to go. I don't want to interrupt my worrying to go.

J. D. SALINGER

DATE

WHY I CAN'T SLEEP TONIGHT:

_____
_____
_____
_____
_____
_____
_____
_____
_____
_____
_____
_____
_____
_____
_____
_____
_____
_____
_____
_____
_____
_____
_____
_____
_____
_____

WHEN TOMORROW OFFICIALLY BECOMES TODAY:

Don't try to solve serious matters in the middle of the night.

PHILIP K. DICK

	DATE	

WHY I CAN'T SLEEP TONIGHT:

_____

_____

_____

WHEN TOMORROW OFFICIALLY BECOMES TODAY:

There is a drowsy state, between sleeping and waking, when you dream more in five minutes with your eyes half open, and yourself half conscious of everything that is passing around you, than you would in five nights with your eyes fast closed and your senses wrapt in perfect unconsciousness.

CHARLES DICKENS

WHY I CAN'T SLEEP TONIGHT:

_____
_____
_____
_____
_____
_____
_____
_____
_____
_____
_____
_____
_____
_____
_____
_____
_____
_____
_____
_____
_____
_____
_____
_____
_____
_____
_____
_____
_____
_____
_____

WHEN TOMORROW OFFICIALLY BECOMES TODAY:

When you have insomnia, you're never really asleep, and you're never really awake.

CHUCK PALAHNIUK

WHY I CAN'T SLEEP TONIGHT:

WHEN TOMORROW OFFICIALLY BECOMES TODAY:

Wanna fly, you got to give up the shit that weighs you down.

TONI MORRISON

WHY I CAN'T SLEEP TONIGHT:

You can't stand up to the night until you understand what's hiding in its shadows.

CHARLES DE LINT

WHY I CAN'T SLEEP TONIGHT:

_____
_____
_____
_____
_____
_____
_____
_____
_____
_____
_____
_____
_____
_____
_____
_____
_____
_____
_____
_____
_____
_____
_____
_____
_____
_____
_____

WHEN TOMORROW OFFICIALLY BECOMES TODAY:

Many things—such as loving, going to sleep, or behaving unaffectedly—are done worst when we try hardest to do them.

C. S. LEWIS

DATE		

WHY I CAN'T SLEEP TONIGHT:

_____

_____

_____

_____

_____

_____

_____

_____

_____

_____

_____

_____

_____

_____

_____

_____

_____

_____

_____

_____

_____

_____

_____

_____

WHEN TOMORROW OFFICIALLY BECOMES TODAY:

You never have to change anything you got up in the middle of the night to write.

SAUL BELLOW

WHY I CAN'T SLEEP TONIGHT:

_____

_____

_____

_____

_____

_____

_____

_____

_____

_____

_____

_____

_____

_____

_____

_____

_____

_____

_____

_____

_____

_____

_____

_____

_____

_____

_____

WHEN TOMORROW OFFICIALLY BECOMES TODAY:

I haven't been to sleep
for over a year. That's
why I go to bed early.
One needs more rest if
one doesn't sleep.

EVELYN WAUGH

DATE

WHY I CAN'T SLEEP TONIGHT:

_____

_____

_____

_____

_____

_____

_____

_____

_____

_____

_____

_____

_____

_____

_____

_____

_____

_____

_____

_____

_____

_____

_____

_____

_____

_____

_____

_____

_____

_____

WHEN TOMORROW OFFICIALLY BECOMES TODAY:

We spend our midday sweat,
  our midnight oil;

We tire the night in thought,
  the day in toil.

FRANCIS QUARLES

DATE

WHY I CAN'T SLEEP TONIGHT:

It's crazy how you can get yourself in a mess sometimes and not even be able to think about it with any sense and yet not be able to think about anything else.

STANLEY KUBRICK

WHY I CAN'T SLEEP TONIGHT:

_____

_____

_____

_____

_____

_____

_____

_____

_____

_____

_____

_____

_____

_____

_____

_____

_____

_____

_____

_____

_____

_____

_____

_____

_____

_____

_____

_____

WHEN TOMORROW OFFICIALLY BECOMES TODAY:

Tomorrow night is nothing but one long sleepless wrestle with yesterday's omissions and regrets.

WILLIAM FAULKNER

DATE

WHY I CAN'T SLEEP TONIGHT:

_____

_____

_____

_____

_____

_____

_____

_____

_____

_____

_____

_____

_____

_____

_____

_____

_____

_____

_____

_____

_____

_____

_____

_____

_____

WHEN TOMORROW OFFICIALLY BECOMES TODAY:

A ruffled mind makes a restless pillow.

CHARLOTTE BRONTË

DATE

WHY I CAN'T SLEEP TONIGHT:

_____

_____

_____

_____

_____

_____

_____

_____

_____

_____

_____

_____

_____

_____

_____

_____

_____

_____

_____

_____

_____

_____

_____

WHEN TOMORROW OFFICIALLY BECOMES TODAY:

If you can't sleep, then get up and do something instead of lying there worrying. It's the worry that gets you, not the lack of sleep.

DALE CARNEGIE

WHY I CAN'T SLEEP TONIGHT:

_____

_____

_____

_____

_____

_____

_____

_____

_____

_____

_____

_____

_____

_____

_____

_____

_____

_____

_____

_____

_____

_____

_____

_____

_____

WHEN TOMORROW OFFICIALLY BECOMES TODAY:

A man's subconscious self is not the ideal companion. It lurks for the greater part of his life in some dark den of its own, hidden away, and emerges only to taunt and deride and increase the misery of a miserable hour.

P. G. WODEHOUSE

WHY I CAN'T SLEEP TONIGHT:

_____

_____

_____

_____

_____

_____

_____

_____

_____

_____

_____

_____

_____

_____

_____

_____

_____

_____

_____

_____

_____

_____

_____

_____

WHEN TOMORROW OFFICIALLY BECOMES TODAY:

I told the doctor
I was overtired,
anxiety ridden,
compulsively active,
constantly depressed,
with recurring fits of
paranoia. Turns out
I'm normal.

JULES FEIFFER

	DATE	

WHY I CAN'T SLEEP TONIGHT:

_____

_____

_____

_____

_____

_____

_____

_____

_____

_____

_____

_____

_____

_____

_____

_____

_____

_____

_____

_____

_____

_____

_____

_____

_____

WHEN TOMORROW OFFICIALLY BECOMES TODAY:

There are two types of people in this world: good and bad. The good sleep better, but the bad seem to enjoy the waking hours much more.

WOODY ALLEN

DATE

WHY I CAN'T SLEEP TONIGHT:

_____
_____
_____
_____
_____
_____
_____
_____
_____
_____
_____
_____
_____
_____
_____
_____
_____
_____
_____
_____
_____
_____
_____
_____
_____

WHEN TOMORROW OFFICIALLY BECOMES TODAY:

How much pain have cost us the evils which have never happened!

THOMAS JEFFERSON

DATE

WHY I CAN'T SLEEP TONIGHT:

_____
_____
_____
_____
_____
_____
_____
_____
_____
_____
_____
_____
_____
_____
_____
_____
_____
_____
_____
_____
_____
_____
_____
_____
_____

WHEN TOMORROW OFFICIALLY BECOMES TODAY:

What hath night to do with sleep?

JOHN MILTON

	DATE	

WHY I CAN'T SLEEP TONIGHT:

_____

_____

_____

_____

_____

_____

_____

_____

_____

_____

_____

_____

_____

_____

_____

_____

_____

_____

_____

_____

_____

_____

_____

_____

_____

_____

_____

WHEN TOMORROW OFFICIALLY BECOMES TODAY:

The heights by great men reached and kept
Were not attained by sudden flight,
But they, while their companions slept,
Were toiling upward in the night.

HENRY WADSWORTH LONGFELLOW

WHY I CAN'T SLEEP TONIGHT:

_____
_____
_____
_____
_____
_____
_____
_____
_____
_____
_____
_____
_____
_____
_____
_____
_____
_____
_____
_____
_____
_____
_____
_____
_____
_____
_____

WHEN TOMORROW OFFICIALLY BECOMES TODAY:

To be too conscious is an illness—
a real thoroughgoing illness.

FYODOR DOSTOYEVSKY

DATE

WHY I CAN'T SLEEP TONIGHT:

_____
_____
_____
_____
_____
_____
_____
_____
_____
_____
_____
_____
_____
_____
_____
_____
_____
_____
_____
_____
_____
_____
_____
_____
_____
_____
_____
_____
_____

WHEN TOMORROW OFFICIALLY BECOMES TODAY:

It is one of life's bitterest truths that bedtime so often arrives just when things are really getting interesting.

LEMONY SNICKET

DATE		

WHY I CAN'T SLEEP TONIGHT:

_____

_____

_____

_____

_____

_____

_____

_____

_____

_____

_____

_____

_____

_____

_____

_____

_____

_____

_____

_____

_____

_____

_____

_____

_____

_____

_____

WHEN TOMORROW OFFICIALLY BECOMES TODAY:

Hello darkness, my old friend
I've come to talk with you again.

———

PAUL SIMON

WHY I CAN'T SLEEP TONIGHT:

_____

_____

_____

_____

_____

_____

_____

_____

_____

_____

_____

_____

_____

_____

_____

_____

_____

_____

_____

_____

_____

_____

_____

_____

WHEN TOMORROW OFFICIALLY BECOMES TODAY:

I often think that the night is more alive and more richly colored than the day.

_____

VINCENT VAN GOGH

DATE

WHY I CAN'T SLEEP TONIGHT:

_____
_____
_____
_____
_____
_____
_____
_____
_____
_____
_____
_____
_____
_____
_____
_____
_____
_____
_____
_____
_____
_____
_____
_____
_____
_____

WHEN TOMORROW OFFICIALLY BECOMES TODAY:

When I feel well and in a good humour, or when I am taking a drive or walking after a good meal, or in the night when I cannot sleep, thoughts crowd into my mind as easily as you could wish.

WOLFGANG AMADEUS MOZART

WHY I CAN'T SLEEP TONIGHT:

_____
_____
_____
_____
_____
_____
_____
_____
_____
_____
_____
_____
_____
_____
_____
_____
_____
_____
_____
_____
_____
_____
_____
_____
_____
_____
_____
_____
_____

WHEN TOMORROW OFFICIALLY BECOMES TODAY:

We are dying from overthinking.
We are slowly killing ourselves by
thinking about everything. Think.
Think. Think. You can never trust
the human mind anyway.
It's a death trap.

ANTHONY HOPKINS

WHY I CAN'T SLEEP TONIGHT:

_____

_____

_____

_____

_____

_____

_____

_____

_____

_____

_____

_____

_____

_____

_____

_____

_____

_____

_____

_____

_____

_____

_____

_____

_____

_____

_____

_____

_____

WHEN TOMORROW OFFICIALLY BECOMES TODAY:

The summer demands and takes away
  too much,

But night, the reserved, the reticent,
  gives more than it takes.

———————————

JOHN ASHBERY

WHY I CAN'T SLEEP TONIGHT:

_____

_____

_____

_____

_____

_____

_____

_____

_____

_____

_____

_____

_____

_____

_____

_____

_____

_____

_____

_____

_____

_____

_____

_____

_____

_____

_____

WHEN TOMORROW OFFICIALLY BECOMES TODAY:

The worst thing in the world is to try to sleep and not to.

F. SCOTT FITZGERALD

DATE		

WHY I CAN'T SLEEP TONIGHT:

_____

_____

_____

_____

_____

_____

_____

_____

_____

_____

_____

_____

_____

_____

_____

_____

_____

_____

_____

_____

_____

_____

_____

_____

_____

_____

_____

_____

_____

WHEN TOMORROW OFFICIALLY BECOMES TODAY:

I have been one acquainted with the night.
I have walked out in rain—and back in rain.
I have outwalked the furthest city light.

ROBERT FROST

DATE

WHY I CAN'T SLEEP TONIGHT:

_____

_____

_____

_____

_____

_____

_____

_____

_____

_____

_____

_____

_____

_____

_____

_____

_____

_____

_____

_____

_____

_____

_____

_____

_____

_____

_____

_____

_____

WHEN TOMORROW OFFICIALLY BECOMES TODAY:

If you're gonna fall apart, do it in your own bedroom.

MARGOT KIDDER

DATE

WHY I CAN'T SLEEP TONIGHT:

_____

_____

_____

_____

_____

_____

_____

_____

_____

_____

_____

_____

_____

_____

_____

_____

_____

_____

_____

_____

_____

_____

_____

_____

_____

_____

_____

_____

WHEN TOMORROW OFFICIALLY BECOMES TODAY:

Fasten your seatbelts.
It's going to be a bumpy night.

JOSEPH L. MANKIEWICZ

DATE

WHY I CAN'T SLEEP TONIGHT:

_____
_____
_____
_____
_____
_____
_____
_____
_____
_____
_____
_____
_____
_____
_____
_____
_____
_____
_____
_____
_____
_____
_____
_____
_____

WHEN TOMORROW OFFICIALLY BECOMES TODAY:

Brave captain, why are the wicked so strong? How do the angels get to sleep when the devil leaves the porch light on?

TOM WAITS

WHY I CAN'T SLEEP TONIGHT:

_____

_____

_____

_____

_____

_____

_____

_____

_____

_____

_____

_____

_____

_____

_____

_____

_____

_____

_____

_____

_____

_____

_____

_____

_____

_____

WHEN TOMORROW OFFICIALLY BECOMES TODAY:

Whoever thinks of going to bed before twelve o'clock is a scoundrel.

SAMUEL JOHNSON

DATE

WHY I CAN'T SLEEP TONIGHT:

_____
_____
_____
_____
_____
_____
_____
_____
_____
_____
_____
_____
_____
_____
_____
_____
_____
_____
_____
_____
_____
_____
_____
_____
_____
_____
_____

WHEN TOMORROW OFFICIALLY BECOMES TODAY:

Sleeplessness is a desert without vegetation or inhabitants.

JESSAMYN WEST

WHY I CAN'T SLEEP TONIGHT:

_____

_____

_____

_____

_____

_____

_____

_____

_____

_____

_____

_____

_____

_____

_____

_____

_____

_____

_____

_____

_____

_____

_____

_____

_____

_____

_____

_____

_____

_____

_____

WHEN TOMORROW OFFICIALLY BECOMES TODAY:

There are nights when the wolves
are silent and only the moon howls.

GEORGE CARLIN

DATE

WHY I CAN'T SLEEP TONIGHT:

_____

_____

_____

_____

_____

_____

_____

_____

_____

_____

_____

_____

_____

_____

_____

_____

_____

_____

_____

_____

_____

_____

_____

_____

WHEN TOMORROW OFFICIALLY BECOMES TODAY:

The best cure for insomnia is to get a lot of sleep.

W. C. FIELDS

DATE

WHY I CAN'T SLEEP TONIGHT:

_____

_____

_____

_____

_____

_____

_____

_____

_____

_____

_____

_____

_____

_____

_____

_____

_____

_____

_____

_____

_____

_____

_____

_____

_____

_____

WHEN TOMORROW OFFICIALLY BECOMES TODAY:

Oh the nerves, the nerves;
the mysteries of this machine
called Man! Oh the little that
unhinges it: poor creatures
that we are!

CHARLES DICKENS

	DATE	

WHY I CAN'T SLEEP TONIGHT:

_____
_____
_____
_____
_____
_____
_____
_____
_____
_____
_____
_____
_____
_____
_____
_____
_____
_____
_____
_____
_____
_____
_____
_____
_____
_____
_____
_____
_____

WHEN TOMORROW OFFICIALLY BECOMES TODAY:

Sleep is the most moronic fraternity in the world, with the heaviest dues and the crudest rituals.

VLADIMIR NABOKOV

WHY I CAN'T SLEEP TONIGHT:

_____
_____
_____
_____
_____
_____
_____
_____
_____
_____
_____
_____
_____
_____
_____
_____
_____
_____
_____
_____
_____
_____
_____
_____
_____
_____

WHEN TOMORROW OFFICIALLY BECOMES TODAY:

Drag your thoughts away from your troubles—by the ears, by the heels, or any other way, so you can manage it.

MARK TWAIN

DATE

WHY I CAN'T SLEEP TONIGHT:

_____
_____
_____
_____
_____
_____
_____
_____
_____
_____
_____
_____
_____
_____
_____
_____
_____
_____
_____
_____
_____
_____
_____
_____
_____

WHEN TOMORROW OFFICIALLY BECOMES TODAY:

So dear night the half of life is,
And the fairest half indeed.

JOHANN WOLFGANG VON GOETHE

DATE		

WHY I CAN'T SLEEP TONIGHT:

_____

_____

_____

_____

_____

_____

_____

_____

_____

_____

_____

_____

_____

_____

_____

_____

_____

_____

_____

_____

_____

_____

_____

_____

_____

_____

_____

_____

WHEN TOMORROW OFFICIALLY BECOMES TODAY:

Dawn, n. The time when men of reason go to bed.

AMBROSE BIERCE

DATE		

WHY I CAN'T SLEEP TONIGHT:

_____
_____
_____
_____
_____
_____
_____
_____
_____
_____
_____
_____
_____
_____
_____
_____
_____
_____
_____
_____
_____
_____
_____
_____
_____

WHEN TOMORROW OFFICIALLY BECOMES TODAY:

From restless thoughts, that,
 like a deadly swarm

Of hornets arm'd, no sooner
 found alone,

But rush upon me thronging.

———

JOHN MILTON

DATE

WHY I CAN'T SLEEP TONIGHT:

_____
_____
_____
_____
_____
_____
_____
_____
_____
_____
_____
_____
_____
_____
_____
_____
_____
_____
_____
_____
_____
_____
_____
_____
_____
_____
_____
_____

WHEN TOMORROW OFFICIALLY BECOMES TODAY:

Don't start me talking
I could talk all night
My mind goes sleepwalking
While I'm putting the world to right.

ELVIS COSTELLO

WHY I CAN'T SLEEP TONIGHT:

_____

_____

_____

_____

_____

_____

_____

_____

_____

_____

_____

_____

_____

_____

_____

_____

_____

_____

_____

_____

_____

_____

_____

_____

_____

_____

_____

WHEN TOMORROW OFFICIALLY BECOMES TODAY:

Most glorious night!
Thou wert not sent
   for slumber!

LORD BYRON

WHY I CAN'T SLEEP TONIGHT:

WHEN TOMORROW OFFICIALLY BECOMES TODAY:

Stop worrying—nobody gets
out of this world alive.

CLIVE JAMES

DATE		

WHY I CAN'T SLEEP TONIGHT:

_____

_____

_____

_____

_____

_____

_____

_____

_____

_____

_____

_____

_____

_____

_____

_____

_____

_____

_____

_____

_____

_____

_____

_____

_____

_____

_____

WHEN TOMORROW OFFICIALLY BECOMES TODAY:

...and so to bed.

SAMUEL PEPYS

DATE

WHY I CAN'T SLEEP TONIGHT:

_____
_____
_____
_____
_____
_____
_____
_____
_____
_____
_____
_____
_____
_____
_____
_____
_____
_____
_____
_____
_____
_____
_____
_____
_____

WHEN TOMORROW OFFICIALLY BECOMES TODAY:

Good morning and good luck.
